IN MY HUMBLE
OPINION

KNOCK KNOCK®
VENICE, CALIFORNIA

Created and published by Knock Knock
Distributed by Who's There Inc.
Venice, CA 90291
knockknockstuff.com

ISBN: 978-160106342-7
UPC: 825703-50076-9

10 9 8 7 6 5 4 3 2

OTHER PEOPLE ARE SO
ANNOYING

If it weren't for all those total idiots, your life would be great. After all, you're a good driver, a sensible friend, a nuanced coworker, a caring mate, and, most of all, you know how to stand in a line without cutting. Given the antics of the thronging rabble, however, "If you're not angry, you're not paying attention," as the bumper sticker says. We might all be better off if we *weren't* paying attention—to the tailgating jerk behind us, the woman screeching into her cell phone, or the waiter who thinks he's God's gift. Centuries before bumper stickers enriched our lives, eighteenth-century poet Thomas Gray said "Ignorance is bliss," and no doubt it's still true. But for better or worse, you don't have the gift of oblivion.

You notice every little irritating tic and injustice and spend your hours wondering why people are like that. And who could blame you? There's a lot to vent about these days, ranging from the significant (war, environmental destruction, the continued popularity of reality television) to smaller, everyday annoyances (pop songs, telemarketers, overpriced coffee) to the philosophical (do humans even *matter* in the cosmos?). We live in congested cities, competing for resources, clogging highways, and generally rubbing up against one another. The damaging effects of such proximity have been proven: in renowned studies on the deliberate overcrowding of rats, high levels of aggression and compromised health were the inevitable result.

Annoyance isn't very good for you, either. Research shows that those with high hostility levels are likely to die younger than those with low or average levels, primarily from heart disease. Anger's effects include the release of hormones adrenaline and noradrenaline, increased heart rate and blood pressure, and the movement of sugar into the bloodstream. But it also appears that we crave anger—as much as sex, food, or drugs: a Vanderbilt University study showed that aggression engages the brain's reward pathways and involves dopamine.

Experts believe that anger is generally best suppressed (not expressed), but that it can be damaging when repressed (not known or acknowledged). Journaling is thus an ideal outlet for aggression: you won't anger anyone else, and you just might work through your own anger. As Kathleen Adams, founder of the Center for Journal Therapy, puts it, journals are "79-cent therapists."

According to a widely cited study by James W. Pennebaker and Janel D. Seagal, "Writing about important personal experiences in an emotional way for as little as fifteen minutes over the course of three days brings about improvements in mental and physical health." Proven benefits include stress management, strengthened immunity, fewer doctor visits, and improvement in chronic illnesses such as asthma. "It's hard to believe," says Pennebaker, a psychology professor at the University of Texas at Austin, but "being able to put experiences into words is good for your physical health." How does this work? Some experts believe organizing experience into a narrative may be beneficial. According to scholarship cited in *Newsweek*, journaling "forces us to transform the ruminations cluttering our minds into coherent stories. Writing about an experience may also dull its emotional impact." Psychologist Ira Progoff, father of the modern journaling movement, stated in 1975 that an "intensive journal process" could "draw each person's life toward wholeness at its own tempo."

To get the most out of the process, here are a few tips: experts agree that you should try to write quasi-daily, for at least 5–15 minutes. For inspiration, famed diarist Anaïs Nin suggests asking yourself, "What feels vivid, warm, or near to you at the moment?" Don't critique your writing; just spew. Finally, choose a home for your journal where others won't find it.

Thomas Jefferson declared, "When angry, count ten, before you speak. If very angry, an hundred." Mark Twain advised, "When angry, count four. When very angry, swear." We say, "When angry, irritated, or bursting with humble opinions, journal."

The world is populated in the main by people who should not exist.

George Bernard Shaw

WHY PEOPLE ARE LIKE THAT TODAY:

_____

_____

_____

_____

_____

_____

_____

_____

_____

_____

_____

_____

_____

_____

_____

_____

_____

_____

TODAY'S DEFINITIVE CONCLUSION ABOUT HUMANITY:

The problem with the
gene pool is that there
is no lifeguard.

Steven Wright

WHY PEOPLE ARE LIKE THAT TODAY:

_____

_____

_____

_____

_____

_____

_____

_____

_____

_____

_____

_____

_____

_____

_____

_____

_____

_____

TODAY'S DEFINITIVE CONCLUSION ABOUT HUMANITY:

I sometimes think that God
in creating man somewhat
overestimated his ability.

Oscar Wilde

WHY PEOPLE ARE LIKE THAT TODAY:

_____

_____

_____

_____

_____

_____

_____

_____

_____

_____

_____

_____

_____

_____

_____

_____

_____

_____

_____

_____

_____

TODAY'S DEFINITIVE CONCLUSION ABOUT HUMANITY:

Human beings, who
are almost unique
in having the ability
to learn from the
experience of others,
are also remarkable
for their apparent
disinclination to do so.

Douglas Adams

WHY PEOPLE ARE LIKE THAT TODAY:

_____

_____

_____

_____

_____

_____

_____

_____

_____

_____

_____

_____

_____

_____

_____

_____

_____

TODAY'S DEFINITIVE CONCLUSION ABOUT HUMANITY:

The world is made up for the most part of morons and natural tyrants, sure of themselves, strong in their own opinions, never doubting anything.

Clarence Darrow

WHY PEOPLE ARE LIKE THAT TODAY:

_____

_____

_____

_____

_____

_____

_____

_____

_____

_____

_____

_____

_____

_____

_____

_____

TODAY'S DEFINITIVE CONCLUSION ABOUT HUMANITY:

Only two things are infinite, the universe and human stupidity, and I'm not sure about the former.

Albert Einstein

WHY PEOPLE ARE LIKE THAT TODAY:

_____

_____

_____

_____

_____

_____

_____

_____

_____

_____

_____

_____

_____

_____

_____

_____

_____

_____

_____

TODAY'S DEFINITIVE CONCLUSION ABOUT HUMANITY:

Many people would sooner die than think. In fact, they do.

Bertrand Russell

WHY PEOPLE ARE LIKE THAT TODAY:

_____

_____

_____

_____

_____

_____

_____

_____

_____

_____

_____

_____

_____

_____

_____

_____

_____

TODAY'S DEFINITIVE CONCLUSION ABOUT HUMANITY:

Maybe this world is another planet's hell.

Aldous Huxley

WHY PEOPLE ARE LIKE THAT TODAY:

_____

_____

_____

_____

_____

_____

_____

_____

_____

_____

_____

_____

_____

_____

_____

_____

_____

_____

TODAY'S DEFINITIVE CONCLUSION ABOUT HUMANITY:

Such is the human race. Often it does seem such a pity that Noah ... didn't miss the boat.

Mark Twain

DATE

WHY PEOPLE ARE LIKE THAT TODAY:

_____

_____

_____

_____

_____

_____

_____

_____

_____

_____

_____

_____

_____

_____

_____

_____

TODAY'S DEFINITIVE CONCLUSION ABOUT HUMANITY:

And isn't your life extremely flat

With nothing whatever
  to grumble at!

W.S. Gilbert

DATE

WHY PEOPLE ARE LIKE THAT TODAY:

_____

_____

_____

_____

_____

_____

_____

_____

_____

_____

_____

_____

_____

_____

_____

_____

_____

TODAY'S DEFINITIVE CONCLUSION ABOUT HUMANITY:

We must, however, acknowledge, as it seems to me, that man with all his noble qualities ... still bears in his bodily frame the indelible stamp of his lowly origin.

Charles Darwin

WHY PEOPLE ARE LIKE THAT TODAY:

_____

_____

_____

_____

_____

_____

_____

_____

_____

_____

_____

_____

_____

_____

_____

_____

_____

TODAY'S DEFINITIVE CONCLUSION ABOUT HUMANITY:

The more humanity advances, the more it is degraded.

Gustave Flaubert

DATE

WHY PEOPLE ARE LIKE THAT TODAY:

_____

_____

_____

_____

_____

_____

_____

_____

_____

_____

_____

_____

_____

_____

_____

_____

TODAY'S DEFINITIVE CONCLUSION ABOUT HUMANITY:

Since I no longer expect
anything from mankind except
madness,
meanness, and mendacity;
egotism,
cowardice,
and
self-delusion,
I have stopped
being a
misanthrope.

Irving Layton

WHY PEOPLE ARE LIKE THAT TODAY:

_____

_____

_____

_____

_____

_____

_____

_____

_____

_____

_____

_____

_____

_____

_____

_____

_____

TODAY'S DEFINITIVE CONCLUSION ABOUT HUMANITY:

I only go
out to get
me a fresh
appetite
for being
alone.

Lord Byron

DATE

WHY PEOPLE ARE LIKE THAT TODAY:

_____

_____

_____

_____

_____

_____

_____

_____

_____

_____

_____

_____

_____

_____

_____

_____

_____

_____

TODAY'S DEFINITIVE CONCLUSION ABOUT HUMANITY:

The Bible tells us to love our neighbors, and also to love our enemies; probably because they are generally the same people.

G. K. Chesterton

DATE

WHY PEOPLE ARE LIKE THAT TODAY:

_____
_____
_____
_____
_____
_____
_____
_____
_____
_____
_____
_____
_____
_____
_____
_____
_____
_____

TODAY'S DEFINITIVE CONCLUSION ABOUT HUMANITY:

It's too bad that stupidity isn't painful.

Anton LaVey

DATE

WHY PEOPLE ARE LIKE THAT TODAY:

_____

_____

_____

_____

_____

_____

_____

_____

_____

_____

_____

_____

_____

_____

_____

_____

_____

_____

TODAY'S DEFINITIVE CONCLUSION ABOUT HUMANITY:

How I *hate* the attitude of ordinary people to life. How I loathe ordinariness! How from my soul I abhor nice simple people, with their eternal price list. It makes my blood boil.

D. H. Lawrence

DATE

WHY PEOPLE ARE LIKE THAT TODAY:

_____

_____

_____

_____

_____

_____

_____

_____

_____

_____

_____

_____

_____

_____

_____

_____

_____

_____

_____

_____

_____

TODAY'S DEFINITIVE CONCLUSION ABOUT HUMANITY:

Everyone is as
God made him,
and often a great
deal worse.

Miguel de Cervantes

WHY PEOPLE ARE LIKE THAT TODAY:

_____

_____

_____

_____

_____

_____

_____

_____

_____

_____

_____

_____

_____

_____

_____

_____

_____

TODAY'S DEFINITIVE CONCLUSION ABOUT HUMANITY:

Some scientists claim that hydrogen, because it is so plentiful, is the basic building block of the universe. I dispute that. I say there is more stupidity than hydrogen, and that is the basic building block of the universe.

Frank Zappa

WHY PEOPLE ARE LIKE THAT TODAY:

_____

_____

_____

_____

_____

_____

_____

_____

_____

_____

_____

_____

_____

_____

_____

_____

_____

_____

TODAY'S DEFINITIVE CONCLUSION ABOUT HUMANITY:

I think everybody's nuts.

Johnny Depp

WHY PEOPLE ARE LIKE THAT TODAY:

_____

_____

_____

_____

_____

_____

_____

_____

_____

_____

_____

_____

_____

_____

_____

_____

_____

_____

_____

_____

_____

TODAY'S DEFINITIVE CONCLUSION ABOUT HUMANITY:

**The chief obstacle
to the progress of
the human race is
the human race.**

Don Marquis

DATE

WHY PEOPLE ARE LIKE THAT TODAY:

_____

_____

_____

_____

_____

_____

_____

_____

_____

_____

_____

_____

_____

_____

_____

_____

_____

_____

_____

_____

_____

TODAY'S DEFINITIVE CONCLUSION ABOUT HUMANITY:

Everyone looks retarded once you set your mind to it.

David Sedaris

WHY PEOPLE ARE LIKE THAT TODAY:

_____

_____

_____

_____

_____

_____

_____

_____

_____

_____

_____

_____

_____

_____

_____

_____

_____

_____

_____

_____

TODAY'S DEFINITIVE CONCLUSION ABOUT HUMANITY:

Cynicism is an unpleasant way of saying the truth.

Lillian Hellman

WHY PEOPLE ARE LIKE THAT TODAY:

_____

_____

_____

_____

_____

_____

_____

_____

_____

_____

_____

_____

_____

_____

_____

_____

_____

_____

TODAY'S DEFINITIVE CONCLUSION ABOUT HUMANITY:

In nature a repulsive caterpillar turns into a lovely butterfly. But with human beings it is the other way around: a lovely butterfly turns into a repulsive caterpillar.

Anton Chekhov

WHY PEOPLE ARE LIKE THAT TODAY:

_____

_____

_____

_____

_____

_____

_____

_____

_____

_____

_____

_____

_____

_____

_____

_____

_____

_____

_____

TODAY'S DEFINITIVE CONCLUSION ABOUT HUMANITY:

The only thing that will be remembered about my enemies after they're dead is the nasty things I've said about them.

Camille Paglia

DATE		

WHY PEOPLE ARE LIKE THAT TODAY:

_____

_____

_____

_____

_____

_____

_____

_____

_____

_____

_____

_____

_____

_____

_____

_____

_____

_____

TODAY'S DEFINITIVE CONCLUSION ABOUT HUMANITY:

A true gentleman
is one who is never
unintentionally rude.

Oscar Wilde

WHY PEOPLE ARE LIKE THAT TODAY:

TODAY'S DEFINITIVE CONCLUSION ABOUT HUMANITY:

Common sense is not so common.

Voltaire

WHY PEOPLE ARE LIKE THAT TODAY:

_____

_____

_____

_____

_____

_____

_____

_____

_____

_____

_____

_____

_____

_____

_____

_____

_____

TODAY'S DEFINITIVE CONCLUSION ABOUT HUMANITY:

The fundamental cause of trouble in the world today is that the stupid are cocksure while the intelligent are full of doubt.

Bertrand Russell

WHY PEOPLE ARE LIKE THAT TODAY:

TODAY'S DEFINITIVE CONCLUSION ABOUT HUMANITY:

Much virtue in herbs, little in men.

Benjamin Franklin

WHY PEOPLE ARE LIKE THAT TODAY:

TODAY'S DEFINITIVE CONCLUSION ABOUT HUMANITY:

When I think of the number
of disagreeable people that
I know who have gone to a
better world, I am sure hell
won't be so bad at all.

Mark Twain

WHY PEOPLE ARE LIKE THAT TODAY:

_____

_____

_____

_____

_____

_____

_____

_____

_____

_____

_____

_____

_____

_____

_____

_____

_____

TODAY'S DEFINITIVE CONCLUSION ABOUT HUMANITY:

Don't overestimate
the decency of
the human race.

H. L. Mencken

WHY PEOPLE ARE LIKE THAT TODAY:

_____

_____

_____

_____

_____

_____

_____

_____

_____

_____

_____

_____

_____

_____

_____

_____

_____

_____

TODAY'S DEFINITIVE CONCLUSION ABOUT HUMANITY:

Perhaps if we saw what was ahead of us, and glimpsed the crimes, follies, and misfortunes that would befall us later on, we would all stay in our mother's wombs, and then there would be nobody in the world but a great number of very fat, very irritated women.

Lemony Snicket

WHY PEOPLE ARE LIKE THAT TODAY:

_____

_____

_____

_____

_____

_____

_____

_____

_____

_____

_____

_____

_____

_____

_____

_____

_____

_____

_____

TODAY'S DEFINITIVE CONCLUSION ABOUT HUMANITY:

Nobody ever lost a nickel betting against the intelligence of the American public.

P. T. Barnum

DATE

WHY PEOPLE ARE LIKE THAT TODAY:

_____

_____

_____

_____

_____

_____

_____

_____

_____

_____

_____

_____

_____

_____

_____

_____

TODAY'S DEFINITIVE CONCLUSION ABOUT HUMANITY:

I don't have pet peeves, I have whole kennels of irritation.

Whoopi Goldberg

WHY PEOPLE ARE LIKE THAT TODAY:

_____

_____

_____

_____

_____

_____

_____

_____

_____

_____

_____

_____

_____

_____

_____

_____

TODAY'S DEFINITIVE CONCLUSION ABOUT HUMANITY:

If I could get my membership fee back, I'd resign from the human race.

Fred Allen

WHY PEOPLE ARE LIKE THAT TODAY:

_____

_____

_____

_____

_____

_____

_____

_____

_____

_____

_____

_____

_____

_____

_____

_____

_____

_____

_____

_____

TODAY'S DEFINITIVE CONCLUSION ABOUT HUMANITY:

No man lives without jostling and being jostled; in all ways he has to elbow himself through the world, giving and receiving offense.

Thomas Carlyle

DATE

WHY PEOPLE ARE LIKE THAT TODAY:

I love humanity; but I hate people.

Edna St. Vincent Millay

WHY PEOPLE ARE LIKE THAT TODAY:

TODAY'S DEFINITIVE CONCLUSION ABOUT HUMANITY:

The world is a
prison in which
solitary confinement
is preferable.

Karl Kraus

WHY PEOPLE ARE LIKE THAT TODAY:

TODAY'S DEFINITIVE CONCLUSION ABOUT HUMANITY:

The nature of men and women—
their essential nature—is so vile
and despicable that if you were to
portray a person as he really is,
no one would believe you.

W. Somerset Maugham

DATE

WHY PEOPLE ARE LIKE THAT TODAY:

_____
_____
_____
_____
_____
_____
_____
_____
_____
_____
_____
_____
_____
_____
_____
_____
_____
_____
_____

TODAY'S DEFINITIVE CONCLUSION ABOUT HUMANITY:

Optimism is the content of small men in high places.

F. Scott Fitzgerald

DATE

WHY PEOPLE ARE LIKE THAT TODAY:

_____
_____
_____
_____
_____
_____
_____
_____
_____
_____
_____
_____
_____
_____
_____
_____
_____
_____

TODAY'S DEFINITIVE CONCLUSION ABOUT HUMANITY:

Just think of how stupid the average person is, and then realize that half of them are even stupider.

George Carlin

WHY PEOPLE ARE LIKE THAT TODAY:

_____

_____

_____

_____

_____

_____

_____

_____

_____

_____

_____

_____

_____

_____

_____

_____

_____

_____

_____

TODAY'S DEFINITIVE CONCLUSION ABOUT HUMANITY:

Humanity is a pigsty, where liars, hypocrites, and the obscene in spirit congregate.

George Moore

WHY PEOPLE ARE LIKE THAT TODAY:

_____

_____

_____

_____

_____

_____

_____

_____

_____

_____

_____

_____

_____

_____

_____

_____

TODAY'S DEFINITIVE CONCLUSION ABOUT HUMANITY:

Human beings cling to their delicious tyrannies, and to their exquisite nonsense ... till death stares them in the face.

Sydney Smith

WHY PEOPLE ARE LIKE THAT TODAY:

_____

_____

_____

_____

_____

_____

_____

_____

_____

_____

_____

_____

_____

_____

_____

_____

_____

_____

_____

TODAY'S DEFINITIVE CONCLUSION ABOUT HUMANITY:

You can get much further with a kind word and a gun than you can with a kind word alone.

Al Capone

DATE

WHY PEOPLE ARE LIKE THAT TODAY:

_____

_____

_____

_____

_____

_____

_____

_____

_____

_____

_____

_____

_____

_____

_____

_____

_____

TODAY'S DEFINITIVE CONCLUSION ABOUT HUMANITY:

I love mankind ... It's people I can't stand!

Charles M. Schulz

WHY PEOPLE ARE LIKE THAT TODAY:

_____

_____

_____

_____

_____

_____

_____

_____

_____

_____

_____

_____

_____

_____

_____

_____

_____

_____

_____

_____

TODAY'S DEFINITIVE CONCLUSION ABOUT HUMANITY:

What can we know?
What are we all?
Poor silly half-brained
things peering out
at the infinite, with
the aspirations
of angels and the
instincts of beasts.

Arthur Conan Doyle

WHY PEOPLE ARE LIKE THAT TODAY:

TODAY'S DEFINITIVE CONCLUSION ABOUT HUMANITY:

All men are intrinsical rascals, and I am only sorry that, not being a dog, I can't bite them.

Lord Byron

WHY PEOPLE ARE LIKE THAT TODAY:

TODAY'S DEFINITIVE CONCLUSION ABOUT HUMANITY:

I sometimes think of what future historians will say of us. A single sentence will suffice for modern man: he fornicated and read the papers.

Albert Camus

DATE

WHY PEOPLE ARE LIKE THAT TODAY:

TODAY'S DEFINITIVE CONCLUSION ABOUT HUMANITY:

People think it must be fun to be a super genius, but they don't realize how hard it is to put up with all the idiots in the world.

Bill Watterson

DATE

WHY PEOPLE ARE LIKE THAT TODAY:

_____

_____

_____

_____

_____

_____

_____

_____

_____

_____

_____

_____

_____

_____

_____

_____

_____

_____

_____

_____

_____

TODAY'S DEFINITIVE CONCLUSION ABOUT HUMANITY:

The world
is a stage,
but the
play is
badly cast.

Oscar Wilde

WHY PEOPLE ARE LIKE THAT TODAY:

TODAY'S DEFINITIVE CONCLUSION ABOUT HUMANITY:

Cabbage, *n.* A familiar kitchen-garden vegetable about as large and wise as a man's head.

Ambrose Bierce

WHY PEOPLE ARE LIKE THAT TODAY:

_____

_____

_____

_____

_____

_____

_____

_____

_____

_____

_____

_____

_____

_____

_____

_____

_____

_____

_____

TODAY'S DEFINITIVE CONCLUSION ABOUT HUMANITY:

I personally think we developed language because of our deep inner need to complain.

Lily Tomlin

DATE

WHY PEOPLE ARE LIKE THAT TODAY:

When they discover the center of the universe, a lot of people will be disappointed to discover they are not it.

Bernard Bailey

DATE

WHY PEOPLE ARE LIKE THAT TODAY:

TODAY'S DEFINITIVE CONCLUSION ABOUT HUMANITY:

Lord, what fools these mortals be!

William Shakespeare

WHY PEOPLE ARE LIKE THAT TODAY:

_____

_____

_____

_____

_____

_____

_____

_____

_____

_____

_____

_____

_____

_____

_____

_____

_____

_____

_____

TODAY'S DEFINITIVE CONCLUSION ABOUT HUMANITY:

What wretched creature
of what wretched kind,

Than man more weak,
calamitous, and blind?

Homer

DATE

WHY PEOPLE ARE LIKE THAT TODAY:

_____
_____
_____
_____
_____
_____
_____
_____
_____
_____
_____
_____
_____
_____
_____
_____
_____
_____
_____
_____
_____

TODAY'S DEFINITIVE CONCLUSION ABOUT HUMANITY:

There are two sides
to every question:
my side and the
wrong side.

Oscar Levant

WHY PEOPLE ARE LIKE THAT TODAY:

TODAY'S DEFINITIVE CONCLUSION ABOUT HUMANITY:

Man is a rational animal—
so at least I have been told.
Throughout a long life, I have
looked diligently for evidence
in favor of this statement, but
so far I have not had the good
fortune to come across it.

Bertrand Russell

DATE

WHY PEOPLE ARE LIKE THAT TODAY:

TODAY'S DEFINITIVE CONCLUSION ABOUT HUMANITY:

My loathings are simple: stupidity, oppression, crime, cruelty, soft music.

Vladimir Nabokov

WHY PEOPLE ARE LIKE THAT TODAY:

_____

_____

_____

_____

_____

_____

_____

_____

_____

_____

_____

_____

_____

_____

_____

_____

_____

_____

_____

TODAY'S DEFINITIVE CONCLUSION ABOUT HUMANITY:

When dealing with people,
let us remember we are not
dealing with creatures of
logic. We are dealing with
creatures of emotion,
creatures bristling with
prejudices and motivated
by pride and vanity.

Dale Carnegie

DATE

WHY PEOPLE ARE LIKE THAT TODAY:

TODAY'S DEFINITIVE CONCLUSION ABOUT HUMANITY:

Humanity i love you because
when you're hard up you pawn your
intelligence to buy a drink ...

e. e. cummings

DATE

WHY PEOPLE ARE LIKE THAT TODAY:

_____

_____

_____

_____

_____

_____

_____

_____

_____

_____

_____

_____

_____

_____

_____

_____

_____

TODAY'S DEFINITIVE CONCLUSION ABOUT HUMANITY:

I am free of all prejudice. I hate everyone equally.

W. C. Fields

WHY PEOPLE ARE LIKE THAT TODAY:

_____

_____

_____

_____

_____

_____

_____

_____

_____

_____

_____

_____

_____

_____

_____

_____

_____

_____

_____

_____

_____

TODAY'S DEFINITIVE CONCLUSION ABOUT HUMANITY:

The earth...has a skin, and this skin has diseases. One of these diseases, for example, is called "man."

Friedrich Nietzsche

DATE

WHY PEOPLE ARE LIKE THAT TODAY:

Early in life I had to choose between honest arrogance and hypocritical humility. I chose the former and have seen no reason to change.

Frank Lloyd Wright

DATE		

WHY PEOPLE ARE LIKE THAT TODAY:

_____

_____

_____

_____

_____

_____

_____

_____

_____

_____

_____

_____

_____

_____

_____

_____

_____

_____

_____

_____

_____

_____

TODAY'S DEFINITIVE CONCLUSION ABOUT HUMANITY:

I regard you with
an indifference
closely bordering
on aversion.

Robert Louis Stevenson

DATE

WHY PEOPLE ARE LIKE THAT TODAY:

_____

_____

_____

_____

_____

_____

_____

_____

_____

_____

_____

_____

_____

_____

_____

_____

_____

_____

_____

TODAY'S DEFINITIVE CONCLUSION ABOUT HUMANITY:

God made everything out of nothing. But the nothingness shows through.

Paul Valéry

WHY PEOPLE ARE LIKE THAT TODAY:

_____

_____

_____

_____

_____

_____

_____

_____

_____

_____

_____

_____

_____

_____

_____

_____

_____

_____

TODAY'S DEFINITIVE CONCLUSION ABOUT HUMANITY:

Happiness in intelligent people
is the rarest thing I know.

Ernest Hemingway

WHY PEOPLE ARE LIKE THAT TODAY:

_____

_____

_____

_____

_____

_____

_____

_____

_____

_____

_____

_____

_____

_____

_____

_____

_____

_____

_____

TODAY'S DEFINITIVE CONCLUSION ABOUT HUMANITY:

The power of accurate observation is commonly called cynicism by those who have not got it.

George Bernard Shaw

DATE

WHY PEOPLE ARE LIKE THAT TODAY:

TODAY'S DEFINITIVE CONCLUSION ABOUT HUMANITY:

I like long walks,
especially when they
are taken by people
who annoy me.

Fred Allen

DATE

WHY PEOPLE ARE LIKE THAT TODAY:

_____

_____

_____

_____

_____

_____

_____

_____

_____

_____

_____

_____

_____

_____

_____

_____

_____

_____

_____

_____

TODAY'S DEFINITIVE CONCLUSION ABOUT HUMANITY:

I have never killed anyone, but I have read some obituary notices with great satisfaction.

Clarence Darrow

DATE

WHY PEOPLE ARE LIKE THAT TODAY:

TODAY'S DEFINITIVE CONCLUSION ABOUT HUMANITY:

The world is a botched job.

Gabriel García Márquez

DATE

WHY PEOPLE ARE LIKE THAT TODAY:

_____
_____
_____
_____
_____
_____
_____
_____
_____
_____
_____
_____
_____
_____
_____
_____
_____
_____
_____

TODAY'S DEFINITIVE CONCLUSION ABOUT HUMANITY:

I've always been interested in people, but I've never liked them.

W. Somerset Maugham

WHY PEOPLE ARE LIKE THAT TODAY:

TODAY'S DEFINITIVE CONCLUSION ABOUT HUMANITY:

We are all worms.
But I do believe that
I am a glow-worm.

Winston Churchill

DATE

WHY PEOPLE ARE LIKE THAT TODAY:

TODAY'S DEFINITIVE CONCLUSION ABOUT HUMANITY:

Just because
you're paranoid
don't mean they're
not after you.

Kurt Cobain

WHY PEOPLE ARE LIKE THAT TODAY:

_____

_____

_____

_____

_____

_____

_____

_____

_____

_____

_____

_____

_____

_____

_____

_____

_____

_____

_____

TODAY'S DEFINITIVE CONCLUSION ABOUT HUMANITY:

Man was made
at the end of the
week's work, when
God was tired.

Mark Twain

WHY PEOPLE ARE LIKE THAT TODAY:

_____

_____

_____

_____

_____

_____

_____

_____

_____

_____

_____

_____

_____

_____

_____

_____

_____

_____

_____

_____

_____

TODAY'S DEFINITIVE CONCLUSION ABOUT HUMANITY:

There are few people whom I really love, and still fewer of whom I think well. The more I see of the world, the more am I dissatisfied with it; and every day confirms my belief of the inconsistency of all human characters, and of the little dependence that can be placed on the appearance of merit or sense.

Jane Austen

WHY PEOPLE ARE LIKE THAT TODAY:

_____

_____

_____

_____

_____

_____

_____

_____

_____

_____

_____

_____

_____

_____

_____

_____

_____

_____

TODAY'S DEFINITIVE CONCLUSION ABOUT HUMANITY:

I prefer rogues to imbeciles, because they sometimes take a rest.

Alexandre Dumas *père*

WHY PEOPLE ARE LIKE THAT TODAY:

_____

_____

_____

_____

_____

_____

_____

_____

_____

_____

_____

_____

_____

_____

_____

_____

_____

_____

TODAY'S DEFINITIVE CONCLUSION ABOUT HUMANITY:

It's hard to be humble
when you're as great
as I am.

Muhammad Ali